Miracle Aligner

Set in Soul

© 2019 Tatiana Media LLC in partnership with Set In Soul LLC

ISBN #: 978-1-949874-90-7

Published by Tatiana Media LLC

All rights reserved. No part of this journal/publication may be reproduced, stored in a retrieval system, or transmitted in any form or by any means, electronic, mechanical, photocopying, recording, scanning, or otherwise, except as permitted under Section 107 or 108 of the 1976 United States Copyright Act whatsoever without express written permission from the author, except in the case of brief quotations embodied in critical articles and reviews. Please refer all pertinent questions to the publisher.

Limit of Liability/Disclaimer of Warranty: While the publisher and author have used their best efforts in preparing this book/journal, they make no representations or warranties with respect to the accuracy or completeness of the contents of this book/journal and specifically disclaim any implied warranties. The advice and strategies contained herein may not be suitable for your situation. You should consult with a professional where appropriate. Neither the publisher nor author shall be liable for any loss of profit or any other emotional, physical, spiritual and mental distress and damages, including but not limited to special, incidental, consequential, or other damages.

For general information on our other products and services, please contact our Customer Support within the United States at support@setinsoul.com.

Tatiana Media LLC as well as Set In Soul LLC publishes its books in a variety of electronic formats. Some content that appears in print may not be available in electronic books.

This Journal Belongs To

____

Dedicated To Every Miracle Ready To Love Me.

Table Of Contents

How To Use This Journal

So many times we utter the words 'I need a miracle' out of desperation and as a last resort after our own physical efforts. Miracles are so amazing because they are surprising and welcome events that can't be explained. They inspire us, bring us joy, and are life-changing. Miracles keep us believing in better. The ability to manifest our desires and usher in miracles is one that needs to be worked on daily. Life is much more exciting when we are able to manifest the desires of our hearts. When a miracle happens, we feel loved and favored so the ability to recognize, give thanks, and summon miracles may be a priority for you. The key to a miracle is to expect without being attached to the result. The key to manifesting is to constantly put in the work that is needed for manifesting. There is spiritual, mental, and physical work required to manifesting and this journal is the place to help you keep track of the work being put in as well as keep track of the miracles and manifestations that unfold before you. The breakthrough you need is so close. This journal will serve as your accountability partner and close friend. This journal is your space to record the work required of you that your spirit is guiding you towards. It's time for you to manifest your heart's desires despite your current situation. Your ability to manifest has everything to do with what you create and welcome into your heart, mind, spirit and physical space. Miracles do happen and they do happen for you. If you are someone who is not a believer in miracles and manifestation, you will have a completely different mindset in the next thirty days after putting in the work needed to break down mindset barriers. If you are already a believer and just want a bit of consistency with manifesting and the welcoming of miracles, this journal will help you with just that. It's time to leave behind everything that is keeping you from getting everything you desire and what God has promised you. It's time to say yes.

We recommend using this journal every morning and every night while you spend time with God in spirit. Fill out each section and set the intention. Write down what you want, what you need, and the work that you are doing. Write down what you are letting go of and more. Keep track of the day to day changes and epiphanies you experience and see what it leads to. This journal is filled with motivational prompts to inspire you and remove doubt. Use the free styling sections to write down positive actions and more. Feel free to write down what you are struggling with and then start to work on it daily. Jeremiah 32:27 states "I am the Lord, the God of all mankind. Is anything too hard for me?' So let's get started.

The Miracle Mind

The Miracle Mind

Do I Believe In Miracles?

If No To The Prompt Above, Why?

If Yes To The First Prompt, Why?

It's Hard For Me To Believe:

Why Do I Feel That Miracles Haven't Happened For Me
(Answer If Applicable)?

The Miracle Mind

My Current Mindset Is:

I Believe Miracles Are:

I Believe Miracles Come From:

The Last Time I Experienced A Miracle:

The First Major Miracle I Remember:

The Miracle Mind

A List Of Miracles That Have Saved Me:

Miracles That I Pray For:

When I Hear Someone Talk About Their Miracles:

The Kinds Of Miracles I Would Like To Manifest:

What I Currently Know About Miracles:

The Miracle Mind

Am I Aligned With The Miracles I Want?

The Biggest Miracle I've Experienced:

What Was I Doing Prior To Experiencing The Above Miracle?

How Did I Feel?

I Am Deserving Of:

The Miracle Mind

I Expect Miracles To Happen For Me:

I Get Discouraged When:

Once I Experience A Miracle, I:

What I Was Told About Miracles:

I Believe Miracles Happen For Me To:

The Miracle Mind

I Want To Believe:

I Need A Miracle To:

Miracles Reveal To Me:

I Believe In Miracles Because (Answer If Applicable):

God Has Revealed To Me:

The Miracle Mind

God Has Shown Me:

My Life Was Forever Changed Because Of:

I Notice:

I Am Grateful For:

Miracles Have Taught Me:

The Miracle Mind

It's Hard To Experience A Miracle When I'm:

________________________________ Always Told Me That Miracles:

In Order For Me To Manifest A Miracle, I Believe I Must:

Lately It's Been Hard Trying To:

I Want To Change:

The Miracle Mind

I Want To Focus On:

I Want To Feel:

I Expect:

I'm Shifting My Mindset From ________________________________ To

____.

My Current Emotional Space Welcomes:

The Miracle Mind

My Current Mental Space Welcomes:

My Current Spiritual Space Welcomes:

I Stopped Being Desperate Over:

Everyday I Am Believing:

The Truth About My Beliefs:

The Miracle Mind

I Believe Miracles Are Formed:

Everyday I Feel Blessed To:

I Want To Experience:

My Life Has Felt:

I Need A Break From:

The Miracle Mind

I Want More Of:

I Want Less Of:

I Currently Pay Attention To:

I Am Tired Of:

Miracles I Know Others Close To Me Are Asking For:

The Miracle Mind

What Kind Of Person Recieves Miracles?

Why Do I Believe What I Wrote In The Previous Prompt?

Am I The Person I Described?

Do I Doubt Miracles Can Happen To Me?

I Will Believe Up Until The Last Minute Of:

The Miracle Mind

What Would Be A Miracle Towards My Health That I Am Expecting?

What Would Be A Miracle Towards My Finances That I Am Expecting?

What Makes What I Want A Miracle?

What Unseen Miracles Do I Believe Are Happening Right Now?

Miracles Have Helped Me To:

The Miracle Mind

How Am I Setting Myself Up To Receive A Miracle?

How Am I Stepping Out Of My Comfort Zone?

How Am I Helping Others?

Do I Feel Aligned With My Life's Purpose?

What Kind Of Low Expectations Do I Currently Hold?

The Miracle Mind

What Kind Of High Expectations Do I Currently Hold?

I Doubt:

A Promise To Myself:

Miracle Positioning

Miracle Positioning

Morning Positioning

Date:

My Intention:

Today's Affirmation:

Today I Am Asking God For:

I Am Grateful For:

Today I Will:

I See Myself (Write What You Envision Yourself Doing Today):

Nightly Positioning

I Am Feeling:

Time:

Today's Miracle (Describe It And How You Felt Receiving It):

Today's Work (Mental, Spiritual And/ Or Physical):

I Trust God With:

Today I Felt Led To:

Today's Epiphany:

I Have Released:

I Am Starting To: ____.

Miracle Positioning

Morning Positioning

Date:

My Intention:

Today's Affirmation:

Today I Am Asking God For:

I Am Grateful For:

Today I Will:

I See Myself (Write What You Envision Yourself Doing Today):

Nightly Positioning

I Am Feeling:

Time:

Today's Miracle (Describe It And How You Felt Receiving It):

Today's Work (Mental, Spiritual And/ Or Physical):

I Trust God With:

Today I Felt Led To:

Today's Epiphany:

I Have Released:

I Am Starting To: ____.

Miracle Positioning

Morning Positioning

Date:

My Intention:

Today's Affirmation:

Today I Am Asking God For:

I Am Grateful For:

Today I Will:

I See Myself (Write What You Envision Yourself Doing Today):

Nightly Positioning

I Am Feeling:

Time:

Today's Miracle (Describe It And How You Felt Receiving It):

Today's Work (Mental, Spiritual And/ Or Physical):

I Trust God With:

Today I Felt Led To:

Today's Epiphany:

I Have Released:

I Am Starting To: ____.

My Vibe:
Positive.

How Do i Believe Manifestation Occurs?

Miracle Positioning

Morning Positioning

Date:

My Intention:

Today's Affirmation:

Today I Am Asking God For:

I Am Grateful For:

Today I Will:

I See Myself (Write What You Envision Yourself Doing Today):

Nightly Positioning

I Am Feeling:

Time:

Today's Miracle (Describe It And How You Felt Receiving It):

Today's Work (Mental, Spiritual And/ Or Physical):

I Trust God With:

Today I Felt Led To:

Today's Epiphany:

I Have Released:

I Am Starting To: ____.

Miracle Positioning

Morning Positioning

Date:

My Intention:

Today's Affirmation:

Today I Am Asking God For:

I Am Grateful For:

Today I Will:

I See Myself (Write What You Envision Yourself Doing Today):

Nightly Positioning

I Am Feeling:

Time:

Today's Miracle (Describe It And How You Felt Receiving It):

Today's Work (Mental, Spiritual And/ Or Physical):

I Trust God With:

Today I Felt Led To:

Today's Epiphany:

I Have Released:

I Am Starting To: ____.

Miracle Positioning

Morning Positioning

Date:

My Intention:

Today's Affirmation:

Today I Am Asking God For:

I Am Grateful For:

Today I Will:

I See Myself (Write What You Envision Yourself Doing Today):

Nightly Positioning

I Am Feeling:

Time:

Today's Miracle (Describe It And How You Felt Receiving It):

Today's Work (Mental, Spiritual And/ Or Physical):

I Trust God With:

Today I Felt Led To:

Today's Epiphany:

I Have Released:

I Am Starting To: ____.

My Miracle Notes

i Just Know.

i Just Know.

i Just Know.

Miracle Positioning

Morning Positioning

Date:

My Intention:

Today's Affirmation:

Today I Will:

Today I Am Asking God For:

I See Myself (Write What You Envision Yourself Doing Today):

I Am Grateful For:

Nightly Positioning

I Am Feeling:

Time:

Today's Miracle (Describe It And How You Felt Receiving It):

Today I Felt Led To:

Today's Work (Mental, Spiritual And/ Or Physical):

Today's Epiphany:

I Trust God With:

I Have Released:

I Am Starting To: ____.

Miracle Positioning

Morning Positioning

Date:

My Intention:

Today's Affirmation:

Today I Am Asking God For:

I Am Grateful For:

Today I Will:

I See Myself (Write What You Envision Yourself Doing Today);

Nightly Positioning

I Am Feeling:

Time:

Today's Miracle (Describe It And How You Felt Receiving It):

Today's Work (Mental, Spiritual And/ Or Physical):

I Trust God With:

Today I Felt Led To:

Today's Epiphany:

I Have Released:

I Am Starting To: ____.

Miracle Positioning

Morning Positioning

Date:

My Intention:

Today's Affirmation:

Today I Am Asking God For:

I Am Grateful For:

Today I Will:

I See Myself (Write What You Envision Yourself Doing Today):

Nightly Positioning

I Am Feeling:

Time:

Today's Miracle (Describe It And How You Felt Receiving It):

Today's Work (Mental, Spiritual And/ Or Physical):

I Trust God With:

Today I Felt Led To:

Today's Epiphany:

I Have Released:

I Am Starting To: ____.

The Time is Right Now.

Repeat: i'm Expecting A Miracle Within The Next 24 Hours.

Miracle Positioning

Morning Positioning

Date:

My Intention:

Today's Affirmation:

Today I Am Asking God For:

I Am Grateful For:

Today I Will:

I See Myself (Write What You Envision Yourself Doing Today):

Nightly Positioning

I Am Feeling:

Time:

Today's Miracle (Describe It And How You Felt Receiving It):

Today's Work (Mental, Spiritual And/ Or Physical):

I Trust God With:

Today I Felt Led To:

Today's Epiphany:

I Have Released:

I Am Starting To: ____.

Miracle Positioning

Morning Positioning

Date:

My Intention:

Today's Affirmation:

Today I Am Asking God For:

I Am Grateful For:

Today I Will:

I See Myself (Write What You Envision Yourself Doing Today):

Nightly Positioning

I Am Feeling:

Time:

Today's Miracle (Describe It And How You Felt Receiving It):

Today's Work (Mental, Spiritual And/ Or Physical):

I Trust God With:

Today I Felt Led To:

Today's Epiphany:

I Have Released:

I Am Starting To: ____.

My Miracle Notes

Miracle Positioning

Morning Positioning

Date:

My Intention:

Today's Affirmation:

Today I Will:

Today I Am Asking God For:

I See Myself (Write What You Envision Yourself Doing Today):

I Am Grateful For:

Nightly Positioning

I Am Feeling:

Time:

Today's Miracle (Describe It And How You Felt Receiving It):

Today I Felt Led To:

Today's Work (Mental, Spiritual And/ Or Physical):

Today's Epiphany:

I Trust God With:

I Have Released:

I Am Starting To: ____.

Miracle Positioning

Morning Positioning

Date:

My Intention:

Today's Affirmation:

Today I Am Asking God For:

I Am Grateful For:

Today I Will:

I See Myself (Write What You Envision Yourself Doing Today):

Nightly Positioning

I Am Feeling:

Time:

Today's Miracle (Describe It And How You Felt Receiving It):

Today's Work (Mental, Spiritual And/ Or Physical):

I Trust God With:

Today I Felt Led To:

Today's Epiphany:

I Have Released:

I Am Starting To: ____.

Everyday i Want To Say To My Upcoming Miracle....

My Miracle Notes

I feel Good Expecting My Blessings.

Miracle Positioning

Morning Positioning

Date:

My Intention:

Today's Affirmation:

Today I Am Asking God For:

I Am Grateful For:

Today I Will:

I See Myself (Write What You Envision Yourself Doing Today):

Nightly Positioning

I Am Feeling:

Time:

Today's Miracle (Describe It And How You Felt Receiving It):

Today's Work (Mental, Spiritual And/ Or Physical):

I Trust God With:

Today I Felt Led To:

Today's Epiphany:

I Have Released:

I Am Starting To: ____.

Miracle Positioning

Morning Positioning

Date:

My Intention:

Today's Affirmation:

Today I Am Asking God For:

I Am Grateful For:

Today I Will:

I See Myself (Write What You Envision Yourself Doing Today):

Nightly Positioning

I Am Feeling:

Time:

Today's Miracle (Describe It And How You Felt Receiving It):

Today's Work (Mental, Spiritual And/ Or Physical):

I Trust God With:

Today I Felt Led To:

Today's Epiphany:

I Have Released:

I Am Starting To: ______________________________.

Miracles Are Organic. i Don't Have To force Anything.

My Miracle Prayer....

Miracle Positioning

Morning Positioning

Date:

My Intention:

Today's Affirmation:

Today I Am Asking God For:

I Am Grateful For:

Today I Will:

I See Myself (Write What You Envision Yourself Doing Today):

Nightly Positioning

I Am Feeling:

Time:

Today's Miracle (Describe It And How You Felt Receiving It):

Today's Work (Mental, Spiritual And/ Or Physical):

I Trust God With:

Today I Felt Led To:

Today's Epiphany:

I Have Released:

I Am Starting To: ____.

Miracle Positioning

Morning Positioning

Date:

My Intention:

Today's Affirmation:

Today's Asking God For:

I Am Grateful For:

Today I Will:

I See Myself (Write What You Envision Yourself Doing Today):

Nightly Positioning

I Am Feeling:

Time:

Today's Miracle (Describe It And How You Felt Receiving It):

Today's Work (Mental, Spiritual And/ Or Physical):

I Trust God With:

Today I Felt Led To:

Today's Epiphany:

I Have Released:

I Am Starting To: ____.

Miracle Positioning

Morning Positioning

Date:

My Intention:

Today's Affirmation:

Today I Am Asking God For:

I Am Grateful For:

Today I Will:

I See Myself (Write What You Envision Yourself Doing Today):

Nightly Positioning

I Am Feeling:

Time:

Today's Miracle (Describe It And How You Felt Receiving It):

Today's Work (Mental, Spiritual And/ Or Physical):

I Trust God With:

Today I Felt Led To:

Today's Epiphany:

I Have Released:

I Am Starting To: ____.

My Miracle Notes

How Do i Pray for A Miracle?

Miracle Positioning

Morning Positioning

Date:

My Intention:

Today's Affirmation:

Today I Am Asking God For:

I Am Grateful For:

Today I Will:

I See Myself (Write What You Envision Yourself Doing Today):

Nightly Positioning

I Am Feeling:

Time:

Today's Miracle (Describe It And How You Felt Receiving It):

Today's Work (Mental, Spiritual And/ Or Physical):

I Trust God With:

Today I Felt Led To:

Today's Epiphany:

I Have Released:

I Am Starting To: ____.

Miracle Positioning

Morning Positioning

Date:

My Intention:

Today's Affirmation:

Today I Am Asking God For:

I Am Grateful For:

Today I Will:

I See Myself (Write What You Envision Yourself Doing Today):

Nightly Positioning

I Am Feeling:

Time:

Today's Miracle (Describe It And How You Felt Receiving It):

Today's Work (Mental, Spiritual And/ Or Physical):

I Trust God With:

Today I Felt Led To:

Today's Epiphany:

I Have Released:

I Am Starting To: ____.

Miracles Happen for Me Because Of The Love God Has for Me.

My Miracle Notes

Miracle Positioning

Morning Positioning

Date:

My Intention:

Today's Affirmation:

Today I Am Asking God For:

I Am Grateful For:

Today I Will:

I See Myself (Write What You Envision Yourself Doing Today):

Nightly Positioning

I Am Feeling:

Time:

Today's Miracle (Describe It And How You Felt Receiving It):

Today's Work (Mental, Spiritual And/ Or Physical):

I Trust God With:

Today I Felt Led To:

Today's Epiphany:

I Have Released:

I Am Starting To: ______________________________.

Miracle Positioning

Morning Positioning

Date:

My Intention:

Today's Affirmation:

Today I Am Asking God For:

I Am Grateful For:

Today I Will:

I See Myself (Write What You Envision Yourself Doing Today):

Nightly Positioning

I Am Feeling:

Time:

Today's Miracle (Describe It And How You Felt Receiving It):

Today's Work (Mental, Spiritual And/ Or Physical):

I Trust God With:

Today I Felt Led To:

Today's Epiphany:

I Have Released:

I Am Starting To: ____.

Miracles Are My Birthright.

What Unexpected Miracle do i Want?

Miracle Positioning

Morning Positioning

Date:

My Intention:

Today's Affirmation:

Today I Am Asking God For:

I Am Grateful For:

Today I Will:

I See Myself (Write What You Envision Yourself Doing Today):

Nightly Positioning

I Am Feeling:

Time:

Today's Miracle (Describe It And How You Felt Receiving It):

Today's Work (Mental, Spiritual And/ Or Physical):

I Trust God With:

Today I Felt Led To:

Today's Epiphany:

I Have Released:

I Am Starting To: ____.

Miracle Positioning

Morning Positioning

Date:

My Intention:

Today's Affirmation:

Today I Am Asking God For:

I Am Grateful For:

Today I Will:

I See Myself (Write What You Envision Yourself Doing Today):

Nightly Positioning

I Am Feeling:

Time:

Today's Miracle (Describe It And How You Felt Receiving It):

Today's Work (Mental, Spiritual And/ Or Physical):

I Trust God With:

Today I Felt Led To:

Today's Epiphany:

I Have Released:

I Am Starting To: ____.

Miracle Positioning

Morning Positioning

Date:

My Intention:

Today's Affirmation:

Today I Am Asking God For:

I Am Grateful For:

Today I Will:

I See Myself (Write What You Envision Yourself Doing Today):

Nightly Positioning

I Am Feeling:

Time:

Today's Miracle (Describe It And How You Felt Receiving It):

Today's Work (Mental, Spiritual And/ Or Physical):

I Trust God With:

Today I Felt Led To:

Today's Epiphany:

I Have Released:

I Am Starting To: ____.

i Only
See What
i Want.

I Am
A
Miracle.

Miracle Positioning

Morning Positioning

Date:

My Intention:

Today's Affirmation:

Today I Am Asking God For:

I Am Grateful For:

Today I Will:

I See Myself (Write What You Envision Yourself Doing Today):

Nightly Positioning

I Am Feeling:

Time:

Today's Miracle (Describe It And How You Felt Receiving It):

Today's Work (Mental, Spiritual And/ Or Physical):

I Trust God With:

Today I Felt Led To:

Today's Epiphany:

I Have Released:

I Am Starting To: ______________________________.

Miracle Positioning

Morning Positioning

Date:

My Intention:

Today's Affirmation:

Today I Am Asking God For:

I Am Grateful For:

Today I Will:

I See Myself (Write What You Envision Yourself Doing Today):

Nightly Positioning

I Am Feeling:

Time:

Today's Miracle (Describe It And How You Felt Receiving It):

Today's Work (Mental, Spiritual And/ Or Physical):

I Trust God With:

Today I Felt Led To:

Today's Epiphany:

I Have Released:

I Am Starting To: ______________________________.

My Miracle Notes

God Creates Everyones' Miracles In Their Own Unique Way.

Miracle Positioning

Morning Positioning

Date:

My Intention:

Today's Affirmation:

Today I Am Asking God For:

I Am Grateful For:

Today I Will:

I See Myself (Write What You Envision Yourself Doing Today):

Nightly Positioning

I Am Feeling:

Time:

Today's Miracle (Describe It And How You Felt Receiving It):

Today's Work (Mental, Spiritual And/ Or Physical):

I Trust God With:

Today I Felt Led To:

Today's Epiphany:

I Have Released:

I Am Starting To: ____.

Miracle Positioning

Morning Positioning

Date:

My Intention:

Today's Affirmation:

Today I Will:

Today I Am Asking God For:

I See Myself (Write What You Envision Yourself Doing Today):

I Am Grateful For:

Nightly Positioning

I Am Feeling:

Time:

Today's Miracle (Describe It And How You Felt Receiving It):

Today I Felt Led To:

Today's Work (Mental, Spiritual And/ Or Physical):

Today's Epiphany:

I Trust God With:

I Have Released:

I Am Starting To: ____.

Miracle Positioning

Morning Positioning

Date:

My Intention:

Today's Affirmation:

Today I Am Asking God For:

I Am Grateful For:

Today I Will:

I See Myself (Write What You Envision Yourself Doing Today):

Nightly Positioning

I Am Feeling:

Time:

Today's Miracle (Describe It And How You Felt Receiving It):

Today's Work (Mental, Spiritual And/ Or Physical):

I Trust God With:

Today I Felt Led To:

Today's Epiphany:

I Have Released:

I Am Starting To: ____.

What i Would Tell Others About Miracles....

Miracle Positioning

Morning Positioning

Date:

My Intention:

Today's Affirmation:

Today I Am Asking God For:

I Am Grateful For:

Today I Will:

I See Myself (Write What You Envision Yourself Doing Today):

Nightly Positioning

I Am Feeling:

Time:

Today's Miracle (Describe It And How You Felt Receiving It):

Today's Work (Mental, Spiritual And/ Or Physical):

I Trust God With:

Today I Felt Led To:

Today's Epiphany:

I Have Released:

I Am Starting To: ____.

Miracle Positioning

Morning Positioning

Date:

My Intention:

Today's Affirmation:

Today I Am Asking God For:

I Am Grateful For:

Today I Will:

I See Myself (Write What You Envision Yourself Doing Today):

Nightly Positioning

I Am Feeling:

Time:

Today's Miracle (Describe It And How You Felt Receiving It):

Today's Work (Mental, Spiritual And/ Or Physical):

I Trust God With:

Today I Felt Led To:

Today's Epiphany:

I Have Released:

I Am Starting To: ____.

Miracle Positioning

Morning Positioning

Date:

My Intention:

Today's Affirmation:

Today I Am Asking God For:

I Am Grateful For:

Today I Will:

I See Myself (Write What You Envision Yourself Doing Today):

Nightly Positioning

I Am Feeling:

Time:

Today's Miracle (Describe It And How You Felt Receiving It):

Today's Work (Mental, Spiritual And/ Or Physical):

I Trust God With:

Today I Felt Led To:

Today's Epiphany:

I Have Released:

I Am Starting To: ______________________________.

Trust Your Dreams, Not Your Thoughts.

My Miracle Notes

Miracle Positioning

Morning Positioning

Date:

My Intention:

Today's Affirmation:

Today I Am Asking God For:

I Am Grateful For:

Today I Will:

I See Myself (Write What You Envision Yourself Doing Today):

Nightly Positioning

I Am Feeling:

Time:

Today's Miracle (Describe It And How You Felt Receiving It):

Today's Work (Mental, Spiritual And/ Or Physical):

I Trust God With:

Today I Felt Led To:

Today's Epiphany:

I Have Released:

I Am Starting To: ____.

Miracle Positioning

Morning Positioning

Date:

My Intention:

Today's Affirmation:

Today I Am Asking God For:

I Am Grateful For:

Today I Will:

I See Myself (Write What You Envision Yourself Doing Today):

Nightly Positioning

I Am Feeling:

Time:

Today's Miracle (Describe It And How You Felt Receiving It):

Today's Work (Mental, Spiritual And/ Or Physical):

I Trust God With:

Today I Felt Led To:

Today's Epiphany:

I Have Released:

I Am Starting To: ____.

Miracle Positioning

Morning Positioning

Date:

My Intention:

Today's Affirmation:

Today I Am Asking God For:

I Am Grateful For:

Today I Will:

I See Myself (Write What You Envision Yourself Doing Today):

Nightly Positioning

I Am Feeling:

Time:

Today's Miracle (Describe It And How You Felt Receiving It):

Today's Work (Mental, Spiritual And/ Or Physical):

I Trust God With:

Today I Felt Led To:

Today's Epiphany:

I Have Released:

I Am Starting To: ____.

faith + focus = Miracles.

I Declare A Miracle Over My Life.

Miracle Positioning

Morning Positioning

Date:

My Intention:

Today's Affirmation:

Today I Am Asking God For:

I Am Grateful For:

Today I Will:

I See Myself (Write What You Envision Yourself Doing Today):

Nightly Positioning

I Am Feeling:

Time:

Today's Miracle (Describe It And How You Felt Receiving It):

Today's Work (Mental, Spiritual And/ Or Physical):

I Trust God With:

Today I Felt Led To:

Today's Epiphany:

I Have Released:

I Am Starting To: ____.

Miracle Positioning

Morning Positioning

Date:

My Intention:

Today's Affirmation:

Today I Am Asking God For:

I Am Grateful For:

Today I Will:

I See Myself (Write What You Envision Yourself Doing Today):

Nightly Positioning

I Am Feeling:

Time:

Today's Miracle (Describe It And How You Felt Receiving It):

Today's Work (Mental, Spiritual And/ Or Physical):

I Trust God With:

Today I Felt Led To:

Today's Epiphany:

I Have Released:

I Am Starting To: ____.

Miracle Positioning

Morning Positioning

Date:

My Intention:

Today's Affirmation:

Today I Am Asking God For:

I Am Grateful For:

Today I Will:

I See Myself (Write What You Envision Yourself Doing Today):

Nightly Positioning

I Am Feeling:

Time:

Today's Miracle (Describe It And How You Felt Receiving It):

Today's Work (Mental, Spiritual And/ Or Physical):

I Trust God With:

Today I Felt Led To:

Today's Epiphany:

I Have Released:

I Am Starting To: ____.

My Miracle Notes

A
Manifestation
Of My
Miracles
Starts Now.

Miracle Positioning

Morning Positioning

Date:

My Intention:

Today's Affirmation:

Today I Am Asking God For:

I Am Grateful For:

Today I Will:

I See Myself (Write What You Envision Yourself Doing Today):

Nightly Positioning

I Am Feeling:

Time:

Today's Miracle (Describe It And How You Felt Receiving It):

Today's Work (Mental, Spiritual And/ Or Physical):

I Trust God With:

Today I Felt Led To:

Today's Epiphany:

I Have Released:

I Am Starting To: ____.

Miracle Positioning

Morning Positioning

Date:

My Intention:

Today's Affirmation:

Today I Am Asking God For:

I Am Grateful For:

Today I Will:

I See Myself (Write What You Envision Yourself Doing Today):

Nightly Positioning

I Am Feeling:

Time:

Today's Miracle (Describe It And How You Felt Receiving It):

Today's Work (Mental, Spiritual And/ Or Physical):

I Trust God With:

Today I Felt Led To:

Today's Epiphany:

I Have Released:

I Am Starting To: ____.

Miracle Positioning

Morning Positioning

Date:

My Intention:

Today's Affirmation:

Today I Am Asking God For:

I Am Grateful For:

Today I Will:

I See Myself (Write What You Envision Yourself Doing Today):

Nightly Positioning

I Am Feeling:

Time:

Today's Miracle (Describe It And How You Felt Receiving It):

Today's Work (Mental, Spiritual And/ Or Physical):

I Trust God With:

Today I Felt Led To:

Today's Epiphany:

I Have Released:

I Am Starting To: ______________________________.

Everyday i Repeat....

Miracle Positioning

Morning Positioning

Date:

My Intention:

Today's Affirmation:

Today I Am Asking God For:

I Am Grateful For:

Today I Will:

I See Myself (Write What You Envision Yourself Doing Today):

Nightly Positioning

I Am Feeling:

Time:

Today's Miracle (Describe It And How You Felt Receiving It):

Today's Work (Mental, Spiritual And/ Or Physical):

I Trust God With:

Today I Felt Led To:

Today's Epiphany:

I Have Released:

I Am Starting To: ____.

Miracle Positioning

Morning Positioning

Date:

My Intention:

Today's Affirmation:

Today I Am Asking God For:

I Am Grateful For:

Today I Will:

I See Myself (Write What You Envision Yourself Doing Today):

Nightly Positioning

I Am Feeling:

Time:

Today's Miracle (Describe It And How You Felt Receiving It):

Today's Work (Mental, Spiritual And/ Or Physical):

I Trust God With:

Today I Felt Led To:

Today's Epiphany:

I Have Released:

I Am Starting To: ____.

Miracle Positioning

Morning Positioning

Date:

My Intention:

Today's Affirmation:

Today I Am Asking God For:

I Am Grateful For:

Today I Will:

I See Myself (Write What You Envision Yourself Doing Today):

Nightly Positioning

I Am Feeling:

Time:

Today's Miracle (Describe It And How You Felt Receiving It):

Today's Work (Mental, Spiritual And/ Or Physical):

I Trust God With:

Today I Felt Led To:

Today's Epiphany:

I Have Released:

I Am Starting To: ____.

Love is Miracle's Twin.

Miracle Positioning

Morning Positioning

Date:

My Intention:

Today's Affirmation:

Today I Am Asking God For:

I Am Grateful For:

Today I Will:

I See Myself (Write What You Envision Yourself Doing Today):

Nightly Positioning

I Am Feeling:

Time:

Today's Miracle (Describe It And How You Felt Receiving It):

Today's Work (Mental, Spiritual And/ Or Physical):

I Trust God With:

Today I Felt Led To:

Today's Epiphany:

I Have Released:

I Am Starting To: ____________________________________.

Miracle Positioning

Morning Positioning

Date:

My Intention:

Today's Affirmation:

Today I Am Asking God For:

I Am Grateful For:

Today I Will:

I See Myself (Write What You Envision Yourself Doing Today):

Nightly Positioning

I Am Feeling:

Time:

Today's Miracle (Describe It And How You Felt Receiving It):

Today's Work (Mental, Spiritual And/ Or Physical):

I Trust God With:

Today I Felt Led To:

Today's Epiphany:

I Have Released:

I Am Starting To: ____.

I Am Committed To....

My Miracle Notes

Miracle Positioning

Morning Positioning

Date:

My Intention:

Today's Affirmation:

Today I Am Asking God For:

I Am Grateful For:

Today I Will:

I See Myself (Write What You Envision Yourself Doing Today):

Nightly Positioning

I Am Feeling:

Time:

Today's Miracle (Describe It And How You Felt Receiving It):

Today's Work (Mental, Spiritual And/Or Physical):

I Trust God With:

Today I Felt Led To:

Today's Epiphany:

I Have Released:

I Am Starting To: ____.

Miracle Positioning

Morning Positioning

Date:

My Intention:

Today's Affirmation:

Today I Am Asking God For:

I Am Grateful For:

Today I Will:

I See Myself (Write What You Envision Yourself Doing Today):

Nightly Positioning

I Am Feeling:

Time:

Today's Miracle (Describe It And How You Felt Receiving It):

Today's Work (Mental, Spiritual And/ Or Physical):

I Trust God With:

Today I Felt Led To:

Today's Epiphany:

I Have Released:

I Am Starting To: ____.

God is Waiting On You.

My Miracle Notes

Miracle Positioning

Morning Positioning

Date:

My Intention:

Today's Affirmation:

Today I Am Asking God For:

I Am Grateful For:

Today I Will:

I See Myself (Write What You Envision Yourself Doing Today):

Nightly Positioning

I Am Feeling:

Time:

Today's Miracle (Describe It And How You Felt Receiving It):

Today's Work (Mental, Spiritual And/ Or Physical):

I Trust God With:

Today I Felt Led To:

Today's Epiphany:

I Have Released:

I Am Starting To: ____.

Miracle Positioning

Morning Positioning

Date:

My Intention:

Today's Affirmation:

Today I Am Asking God For:

I Am Grateful For:

Today I Will:

I See Myself (Write What You Envision Yourself Doing Today):

Nightly Positioning

I Am Feeling:

Time:

Today's Miracle (Describe It And How You Felt Receiving It):

Today's Work (Mental, Spiritual And/ Or Physical):

I Trust God With:

Today I Felt Led To:

Today's Epiphany:

I Have Released:

I Am Starting To: ____.

Miracle Positioning

Morning Positioning

Date:

My Intention:

Today's Affirmation:

Today I Will:

Today I Am Asking God For:

I See Myself (Write What You Envision Yourself Doing Today):

I Am Grateful For:

Nightly Positioning

I Am Feeling:

Time:

Today's Miracle (Describe It And How You Felt Receiving It):

Today I Felt Led To:

Today's Work (Mental, Spiritual And/ Or Physical):

Today's Epiphany:

I Trust God With:

I Have Released:

I Am Starting To: ______________________________________.

God, i Pray for the Ability To Recognize My Miracles.

i Am Denouncing All Negative Energy That is Shifting My Upcoming Miracles.

Miracle Positioning

Morning Positioning

Date:

My Intention:

Today's Affirmation:

Today I Am Asking God For:

I Am Grateful For:

Today I Will:

I See Myself (Write What You Envision Yourself Doing Today):

Nightly Positioning

I Am Feeling:

Time:

Today's Miracle (Describe It And How You Felt Receiving It):

Today's Work (Mental, Spiritual And/ Or Physical):

I Trust God With:

Today I Felt Led To:

Today's Epiphany:

I Have Released:

I Am Starting To: ______________________________.

Miracle Positioning

Morning Positioning

Date:

My Intention:

Today's Affirmation:

Today I Am Asking God For:

I Am Grateful For:

Today I Will:

I See Myself (Write What You Envision Yourself Doing Today):

Nightly Positioning

I Am Feeling:

Time:

Today's Miracle (Describe It And How You Felt Receiving It):

Today's Work (Mental, Spiritual And/ Or Physical):

I Trust God With:

Today I Felt Led To:

Today's Epiphany:

I Have Released:

I Am Starting To: ____.

Miracle Positioning

Morning Positioning

Date:

My Intention:

Today's Affirmation:

Today I Am Asking God For:

I Am Grateful For:

Today I Will:

I See Myself (Write What You Envision Yourself Doing Today):

Nightly Positioning

I Am Feeling:

Time:

Today's Miracle (Describe It And How You Felt Receiving It):

Today's Work (Mental, Spiritual And/ Or Physical):

I Trust God With:

Today I Felt Led To:

Today's Epiphany:

I Have Released:

I Am Starting To: ____.

The Disbeliefs i Am Releasing....

My Miracle Notes

Miracle Positioning

Morning Positioning

Date:

My Intention:

Today's Affirmation:

Today I Am Asking God For:

I Am Grateful For:

Today I Will:

I See Myself (Write What You Envision Yourself Doing Today):

Nightly Positioning

I Am Feeling:

Time:

Today's Miracle (Describe It And How You Felt Receiving It):

Today's Work (Mental, Spiritual And/ Or Physical):

I Trust God With:

Today I Felt Led To:

Today's Epiphany:

I Have Released:

I Am Starting To: ____.

i Believe i Am Being Guided Towards....

i Think Big, That's Why i Get Big.

Miracle Positioning

Morning Positioning

Date:

My Intention:

Today's Affirmation:

Today I Will:

Today I Am Asking God For:

I See Myself (Write What You Envision Yourself Doing Today):

I Am Grateful For:

Nightly Positioning

I Am Feeling:

Time:

Today's Miracle (Describe It And How You Felt Receiving It):

Today I Felt Led To:

Today's Work (Mental, Spiritual And/ Or Physical):

Today's Epiphany:

I Trust God With:

I Have Released:

I Am Starting To: ____.

Miracle Positioning

Morning Positioning

Date:

My Intention:

Today's Affirmation:

Today I Am Asking God For:

I Am Grateful For:

Today I Will:

I See Myself (Write What You Envision Yourself Doing Today):

Nightly Positioning

I Am Feeling:

Time:

Today's Miracle (Describe It And How You Felt Receiving It):

Today's Work (Mental, Spiritual And/ Or Physical):

I Trust God With:

Today I Felt Led To:

Today's Epiphany:

I Have Released:

I Am Starting To: ____.

Miracle Positioning

Morning Positioning

Date:

My Intention:

Today's Affirmation:

Today I Am Asking God For:

I Am Grateful For:

Today I Will:

I See Myself (Write What You Envision Yourself Doing Today):

Nightly Positioning

I Am Feeling:

Time:

Today's Miracle (Describe It And How You Felt Receiving It):

Today's Work (Mental, Spiritual And/ Or Physical):

I Trust God With:

Today I Felt Led To:

Today's Epiphany:

I Have Released:

I Am Starting To: ______________________________.

My Miracle Notes

The feelings i Want To Experience....

Miracle Positioning

Morning Positioning

Date:

My Intention:

Today's Affirmation:

Today I Am Asking God For:

I Am Grateful For:

Today I Will:

I See Myself (Write What You Envision Yourself Doing Today):

Nightly Positioning

I Am Feeling:

Time:

Today's Miracle (Describe It And How You Felt Receiving It):

Today's Work (Mental, Spiritual And/ Or Physical):

I Trust God With:

Today I Felt Led To:

Today's Epiphany:

I Have Released:

I Am Starting To: ____.

Miracle Positioning

Morning Positioning

Date:

My Intention:

Today's Affirmation:

Today I Am Asking God For:

I Am Grateful For:

Today I Will:

I See Myself (Write What You Envision Yourself Doing Today):

Nightly Positioning

I Am Feeling:

Time:

Today's Miracle (Describe It And How You Felt Receiving It):

Today's Work (Mental, Spiritual And/ Or Physical):

I Trust God With:

Today I Felt Led To:

Today's Epiphany:

I Have Released:

I Am Starting To: ____.

i Deserve What i Believe.

Miracle Positioning

Morning Positioning

Date:

My Intention:

Today's Affirmation:

Today I Am Asking God For:

I Am Grateful For:

Today I Will:

I See Myself (Write What You Envision Yourself Doing Today):

Nightly Positioning

I Am Feeling:

Time:

Today's Miracle (Describe It And How You Felt Receiving It):

Today's Work (Mental, Spiritual And/ Or Physical):

I Trust God With:

Today I Felt Led To:

Today's Epiphany:

I Have Released:

I Am Starting To: ____.

Miracle Positioning

Morning Positioning

Date:

My Intention:

Today's Affirmation:

Today I Am Asking God For:

I Am Grateful For:

Today I Will:

I See Myself (Write What You Envision Yourself Doing Today):

Nightly Positioning

I Am Feeling:

Time:

Today's Miracle (Describe It And How You Felt Receiving It):

Today's Work (Mental, Spiritual And/ Or Physical):

I Trust God With:

Today I Felt Led To:

Today's Epiphany:

I Have Released:

I Am Starting To: ____.

My Miracle Notes

Miracle Positioning

Morning Positioning

Date:

My Intention:

Today's Affirmation:

Today I Will:

Today I Am Asking God For:

I See Myself (Write What You Envision Yourself Doing Today):

I Am Grateful For:

Nightly Positioning

I Am Feeling:

Time:

Today's Miracle (Describe It And How You Felt Receiving It):

Today I Felt Led To:

Today's Work (Mental, Spiritual And/ Or Physical):

Today's Epiphany:

I Trust God With:

I Have Released:

I Am Starting To: ____.

Miracle Positioning

Morning Positioning

Date:

My Intention:

Today's Affirmation:

Today I Am Asking God For:

I Am Grateful For:

Today I Will:

I See Myself (Write What You Envision Yourself Doing Today):

Nightly Positioning

I Am Feeling:

Time:

Today's Miracle (Describe It And How You Felt Receiving It):

Today's Work (Mental, Spiritual And/ Or Physical):

I Trust God With:

Today I Felt Led To:

Today's Epiphany:

I Have Released:

I Am Starting To: ______________________________.

i Make time To Manifest My Miracles By....

Being Realistic Means Expecting Miracles.

Miracle Positioning

Morning Positioning

Date:

My Intention:

Today's Affirmation:

Today I Am Asking God For:

I Am Grateful For:

Today I Will:

I See Myself (Write What You Envision Yourself Doing Today):

Nightly Positioning

I Am Feeling:

Time:

Today's Miracle (Describe It And How You Felt Receiving It):

Today's Work (Mental, Spiritual And/ Or Physical):

I Trust God With:

Today I Felt Led To:

Today's Epiphany:

I Have Released:

I Am Starting To: ____.

Miracle Positioning

Morning Positioning

Date:

My Intention:

Today's Affirmation:

Today I Am Asking God For:

I Am Grateful For:

Today I Will:

I See Myself (Write What You Envision Yourself Doing Today):

Nightly Positioning

I Am Feeling:

Time:

Today's Miracle (Describe It And How You Felt Receiving It):

Today's Work (Mental, Spiritual And/ Or Physical):

I Trust God With:

Today I Felt Led To:

Today's Epiphany:

I Have Released:

I Am Starting To: ____.

Miracle Positioning

Morning Positioning

Date:

My Intention:

Today's Affirmation:

Today I Am Asking God For:

I Am Grateful For:

Today I Will:

I See Myself (Write What You Envision Yourself Doing Today):

Nightly Positioning

I Am Feeling:

Time:

Today's Miracle (Describe It And How You Felt Receiving It):

Today's Work (Mental, Spiritual And/ Or Physical):

I Trust God With:

Today I Felt Led To:

Today's Epiphany:

I Have Released:

I Am Starting To: ____.

Miracle Positioning

Morning Positioning

Date:

My Intention:

Today's Affirmation:

Today I Am Asking God For:

I Am Grateful For:

Today I Will:

I See Myself (Write What You Envision Yourself Doing Today):

Nightly Positioning

I Am Feeling:

Time:

Today's Miracle (Describe It And How You Felt Receiving It):

Today's Work (Mental, Spiritual And/ Or Physical):

I Trust God With:

Today I Felt Led To:

Today's Epiphany:

I Have Released:

I Am Starting To: ____.

My Miracle Notes

Miracle Positioning

Morning Positioning

Date:

My Intention:

Today's Affirmation:

Today I Am Asking God For:

I Am Grateful For:

Today I Will:

I See Myself (Write What You Envision Yourself Doing Today):

Nightly Positioning

I Am Feeling:

Time:

Today's Miracle (Describe It And How You Felt Receiving It):

Today's Work (Mental, Spiritual And/ Or Physical):

I Trust God With:

Today I Felt Led To:

Today's Epiphany:

I Have Released:

I Am Starting To: ____.

Miracle Positioning

Morning Positioning

Date:

My Intention:

Today's Affirmation:

Today I Am Asking God For:

I Am Grateful For:

Today I Will:

I See Myself (Write What You Envision Yourself Doing Today):

Nightly Positioning

I Am Feeling:

Time:

Today's Miracle (Describe It And How You Felt Receiving It):

Today's Work (Mental, Spiritual And/ Or Physical):

I Trust God With:

Today I Felt Led To:

Today's Epiphany:

I Have Released:

I Am Starting To: ____.

i Just Know....

Miracle Positioning

Morning Positioning

Date:

My Intention:

Today's Affirmation:

Today I Am Asking God For:

I Am Grateful For:

Today I Will:

I See Myself (Write What You Envision Yourself Doing Today):

Nightly Positioning

I Am Feeling:

Time:

Today's Miracle (Describe It And How You Felt Receiving It):

Today's Work (Mental, Spiritual And/ Or Physical):

I Trust God With:

Today I Felt Led To:

Today's Epiphany:

I Have Released:

I Am Starting To: ____.

Miracle Positioning

Morning Positioning

Date:

My Intention:

Today's Affirmation:

Today I Am Asking God For:

I Am Grateful For:

Today I Will:

I See Myself (Write What You Envision Yourself Doing Today):

Nightly Positioning

I Am Feeling:

Time:

Today's Miracle (Describe It And How You Felt Receiving It):

Today's Work (Mental, Spiritual And/ Or Physical):

I Trust God With:

Today I Felt Led To:

Today's Epiphany:

I Have Released:

I Am Starting To: ____.

Miracle Positioning

Morning Positioning

Date:

My Intention:

Today's Affirmation:

Today I Am Asking God For:

I Am Grateful For:

Today I Will:

I See Myself (Write What You Envision Yourself Doing Today):

Nightly Positioning

I Am Feeling:

Time:

Today's Miracle (Describe It And How You Felt Receiving It):

Today's Work (Mental, Spiritual And/ Or Physical):

I Trust God With:

Today I Felt Led To:

Today's Epiphany:

I Have Released:

I Am Starting To: ______________________________.

Miracle Positioning

Morning Positioning

Date:

My Intention:

Today's Affirmation:

Today I Am Asking God For:

I Am Grateful For:

Today I Will:

I See Myself (Write What You Envision Yourself Doing Today):

Nightly Positioning

I Am Feeling:

Time:

Today's Miracle (Describe It And How You Felt Receiving It):

Today's Work (Mental, Spiritual And/ Or Physical):

I Trust God With:

Today I Felt Led To:

Today's Epiphany:

I Have Released:

I Am Starting To: ____.

i Am

The

Result Of

Belief.

My Miracle Notes

Miracle Positioning

Morning Positioning

Date:

My Intention:

Today's Affirmation:

Today I Am Asking God For:

I Am Grateful For:

Today I Will:

I See Myself (Write What You Envision Yourself Doing Today):

Nightly Positioning

I Am Feeling:

Time:

Today's Miracle (Describe It And How You Felt Receiving It):

Today's Work (Mental, Spiritual And/ Or Physical):

I Trust God With:

Today I Felt Led To:

Today's Epiphany:

I Have Released:

I Am Starting To: ______________________________.

Miracle Positioning

Morning Positioning

Date:

My Intention:

Today's Affirmation:

Today I Am Asking God For:

I Am Grateful For:

Today I Will:

I See Myself (Write What You Envision Yourself Doing Today):

Nightly Positioning

I Am Feeling:

Time:

Today's Miracle (Describe It And How You Felt Receiving It):

Today's Work (Mental, Spiritual And/ Or Physical):

I Trust God With:

Today I Felt Led To:

Today's Epiphany:

I Have Released:

I Am Starting To: ____.

i Am Surrendering....

Miracle Positioning

Morning Positioning

Date:

My Intention:

Today's Affirmation:

Today I Am Asking God For:

I Am Grateful For:

Today I Will:

I See Myself (Write What You Envision Yourself Doing Today):

Nightly Positioning

I Am Feeling:

Time:

Today's Miracle (Describe It And How You Felt Receiving It):

Today's Work (Mental, Spiritual And/ Or Physical):

I Trust God With:

Today I Felt Led To:

Today's Epiphany:

I Have Released:

I Am Starting To: ____.

Miracle Positioning

Morning Positioning

Date:

My Intention:

Today's Affirmation:

Today I Am Asking God For:

I Am Grateful For:

Today I Will:

I See Myself (Write What You Envision Yourself Doing Today):

Nightly Positioning

I Am Feeling:

Time:

Today's Miracle (Describe It And How You Felt Receiving It):

Today's Work (Mental, Spiritual And/ Or Physical):

I Trust God With:

Today I Felt Led To:

Today's Epiphany:

I Have Released:

I Am Starting To: ____.

it Wasnt
By
Mistake,
But By His
Miracles.

I Own
My
Dreams.

Miracle Positioning

Morning Positioning

Date:

My Intention:

Today's Affirmation:

Today I Am Asking God For:

I Am Grateful For:

Today I Will:

I See Myself (Write What You Envision Yourself Doing Today):

Nightly Positioning

I Am Feeling:

Time:

Today's Miracle (Describe It And How You Felt Receiving It):

Today's Work (Mental, Spiritual And/ Or Physical):

I Trust God With:

Today I Felt Led To:

Today's Epiphany:

I Have Released:

I Am Starting To: ____.

Miracle Positioning

Morning Positioning

Date:

My Intention:

Today's Affirmation:

Today I Am Asking God For:

I Am Grateful For:

Today I Will:

I See Myself (Write What You Envision Yourself Doing Today):

Nightly Positioning

I Am Feeling:

Time:

Today's Miracle (Describe It And How You Felt Receiving It):

Today's Work (Mental, Spiritual And/ Or Physical):

I Trust God With:

Today I Felt Led To:

Today's Epiphany:

I Have Released:

I Am Starting To: ____.

Miracle Positioning

Morning Positioning

Date:

My Intention:

Today's Affirmation:

Today I Am Asking God For:

I Am Grateful For:

Today I Will:

I See Myself (Write What You Envision Yourself Doing Today):

Nightly Positioning

I Am Feeling:

Time:

Today's Miracle (Describe It And How You Felt Receiving It):

Today's Work (Mental, Spiritual And/ Or Physical):

I Trust God With:

Today I Felt Led To:

Today's Epiphany:

I Have Released:

I Am Starting To: ____.

My Miracle Notes

My
Winning is
Determined
By My
faith.

Miracle Positioning

Morning Positioning

Date:

My Intention:

Today's Affirmation:

Today I Am Asking God For:

I Am Grateful For:

Today I Will:

I See Myself (Write What You Envision Yourself Doing Today):

Nightly Positioning

I Am Feeling:

Time:

Today's Miracle (Describe It And How You Felt Receiving It):

Today's Work (Mental, Spiritual And/ Or Physical):

I Trust God With:

Today I Felt Led To:

Today's Epiphany:

I Have Released:

I Am Starting To: ____.

Miracle Positioning

Morning Positioning

Date:

My Intention:

Today's Affirmation:

Today I Am Asking God For:

I Am Grateful For:

Today I Will:

I See Myself (Write What You Envision Yourself Doing Today):

Nightly Positioning

I Am Feeling:

Time:

Today's Miracle (Describe It And How You Felt Receiving It):

Today's Work (Mental, Spiritual And/ Or Physical):

I Trust God With:

Today I Felt Led To:

Today's Epiphany:

I Have Released:

I Am Starting To: ____.

What Am i Giving Today?

My Miracle Notes

Miracle Positioning

Morning Positioning

Date:

My Intention:

Today's Affirmation:

Today I Am Asking God For:

I Am Grateful For:

Today I Will:

I See Myself (Write What You Envision Yourself Doing Today):

Nightly Positioning

I Am Feeling:

Time:

Today's Miracle (Describe It And How You Felt Receiving It):

Today's Work (Mental, Spiritual And/ Or Physical):

I Trust God With:

Today I Felt Led To:

Today's Epiphany:

I Have Released:

I Am Starting To: ____.

Miracle Positioning

Morning Positioning

Date:

My Intention:

Today's Affirmation:

Today I Am Asking God For:

I Am Grateful For:

Today I Will:

I See Myself (Write What You Envision Yourself Doing Today):

Nightly Positioning

I Am Feeling:

Time:

Today's Miracle (Describe It And How You Felt Receiving It):

Today's Work (Mental, Spiritual And/ Or Physical):

I Trust God With:

Today I Felt Led To:

Today's Epiphany:

I Have Released:

I Am Starting To: ____.

Life is A Miracle.

The Things That Are Synchronizing Up....

Miracle Positioning

Morning Positioning

Date:

My Intention:

Today's Affirmation:

Today I Will:

Today I Am Asking God For:

I See Myself (Write What You Envision Yourself Doing Today):

I Am Grateful For:

Nightly Positioning

I Am Feeling:

Time:

Today's Miracle (Describe It And How You Felt Receiving It):

Today I Felt Led To:

Today's Work (Mental, Spiritual And/ Or Physical):

Today's Epiphany:

I Trust God With:

I Have Released:

I Am Starting To: ____.

i Prepare for My Miracles....

Miracle Positioning

Morning Positioning

Date:

My Intention:

Today's Affirmation:

Today I Am Asking God For:

I Am Grateful For:

Today I Will:

I See Myself (Write What You Envision Yourself Doing Today):

Nightly Positioning

I Am Feeling:

Time:

Today's Miracle (Describe It And How You Felt Receiving It):

Today's Work (Mental, Spiritual And/ Or Physical):

I Trust God With:

Today I Felt Led To:

Today's Epiphany:

I Have Released:

I Am Starting To: ____.

Miracle Positioning

Morning Positioning

Date:

My Intention:

Today's Affirmation:

Today I Am Asking God For:

I Am Grateful For:

Today I Will:

I See Myself (Write What You Envision Yourself Doing Today):

Nightly Positioning

I Am Feeling:

Time:

Today's Miracle (Describe It And How You Felt Receiving It):

Today's Work (Mental, Spiritual And/ Or Physical):

I Trust God With:

Today I Felt Led To:

Today's Epiphany:

I Have Released:

I Am Starting To: ____.

Miracle Positioning

Morning Positioning

Date:

My Intention:

Today's Affirmation:

Today I Am Asking God For:

I Am Grateful For:

Today I Will:

I See Myself (Write What You Envision Yourself Doing Today):

Nightly Positioning

I Am Feeling:

Time:

Today's Miracle (Describe It And How You Felt Receiving It):

Today's Work (Mental, Spiritual And/ Or Physical):

I Trust God With:

Today I Felt Led To:

Today's Epiphany:

I Have Released:

I Am Starting To: ____.

Miracle Positioning

Morning Positioning

Date:

My Intention:

Today's Affirmation:

Today I Am Asking God For:

I Am Grateful For:

Today I Will:

I See Myself (Write What You Envision Yourself Doing Today):

Nightly Positioning

I Am Feeling:

Time:

Today's Miracle (Describe It And How You Felt Receiving It):

Today's Work (Mental, Spiritual And/ Or Physical):

I Trust God With:

Today I Felt Led To:

Today's Epiphany:

I Have Released:

I Am Starting To: ____.

My Miracle Notes

Miracle Positioning

Morning Positioning

Date:

My Intention:

Today's Affirmation:

Today I Am Asking God For:

I Am Grateful For:

Today I Will:

I See Myself (Write What You Envision Yourself Doing Today):

Nightly Positioning

I Am Feeling:

Time:

Today's Miracle (Describe It And How You Felt Receiving It):

Today's Work (Mental, Spiritual And/ Or Physical):

I Trust God With:

Today I Felt Led To:

Today's Epiphany:

I Have Released:

I Am Starting To: ____.

Miracle Positioning

Morning Positioning

Date:

My Intention:

Today's Affirmation:

Today I Am Asking God For:

I Am Grateful For:

Today I Will:

I See Myself (Write What You Envision Yourself Doing Today):

Nightly Positioning

I Am Feeling:

Time:

Today's Miracle (Describe It And How You Felt Receiving It):

Today's Work (Mental, Spiritual And/ Or Physical):

I Trust God With:

Today I Felt Led To:

Today's Epiphany:

I Have Released:

I Am Starting To: ____.

Miracle Positioning

Morning Positioning

Date:

My Intention:

Today's Affirmation:

Today I Am Asking God For:

I Am Grateful For:

Today I Will:

I See Myself (Write What You Envision Yourself Doing Today):

Nightly Positioning

I Am Feeling:

Time:

Today's Miracle (Describe It And How You Felt Receiving It):

Today's Work (Mental, Spiritual And/ Or Physical):

I Trust God With:

Today I Felt Led To:

Today's Epiphany:

I Have Released:

I Am Starting To: ____.

No Path is Perfect, No Man is Perfect, But God's Divine intervention is. God's Divine intervention is Perfect.

10 Things i Would Love To Do Right Now....

1:

2:

3:

4:

5:

6:

7:

8:

9:

10:

Miracle Positioning

Morning Positioning

Date:

My Intention:

Today's Affirmation:

Today I Am Asking God For:

I Am Grateful For:

Today I Will:

I See Myself (Write What You Envision Yourself Doing Today):

Nightly Positioning

I Am Feeling:

Time:

Today's Miracle (Describe It And How You Felt Receiving It):

Today's Work (Mental, Spiritual And/ Or Physical):

I Trust God With:

Today I Felt Led To:

Today's Epiphany:

I Have Released:

I Am Starting To: ____.

Miracle Positioning

Morning Positioning

Date:

My Intention:

Today's Affirmation:

Today I Am Asking God For:

I Am Grateful For:

Today I Will:

I See Myself (Write What You Envision Yourself Doing Today):

Nightly Positioning

I Am Feeling:

Time:

Today's Miracle (Describe It And How You Felt Receiving It):

Today's Work (Mental, Spiritual And/ Or Physical):

I Trust God With:

Today I Felt Led To:

Today's Epiphany:

I Have Released:

I Am Starting To: ______________________________.

My Miracle Notes

God Gave Me
The Ability
To Manifest.
i Choose To
Manifest Good
in My Life.

Miracle Positioning

Morning Positioning

Date:

My Intention:

Today's Affirmation:

Today I Am Asking God For:

I Am Grateful For:

Today I Will:

I See Myself (Write What You Envision Yourself Doing Today):

Nightly Positioning

I Am Feeling:

Time:

Today's Miracle (Describe It And How You Felt Receiving It):

Today's Work (Mental, Spiritual And/ Or Physical):

I Trust God With:

Today I Felt Led To:

Today's Epiphany:

I Have Released:

I Am Starting To: ____.

Miracle Positioning

Morning Positioning

Date:

My Intention:

Today's Affirmation:

Today I Am Asking God For:

I Am Grateful For:

Today I Will:

I See Myself (Write What You Envision Yourself Doing Today):

Nightly Positioning

I Am Feeling:

Time:

Today's Miracle (Describe It And How You Felt Receiving It):

Today's Work (Mental, Spiritual And/ Or Physical):

I Trust God With:

Today I Felt Led To:

Today's Epiphany:

I Have Released:

I Am Starting To: ____.

Miracle Positioning

Morning Positioning

Date:

My Intention:

Today's Affirmation:

Today I Will:

Today I Am Asking God For:

I See Myself (Write What You Envision Yourself Doing Today):

I Am Grateful For:

Nightly Positioning

I Am Feeling:

Time:

Today's Miracle (Describe It And How You Felt Receiving It):

Today I Felt Led To:

Today's Work (Mental, Spiritual And/ Or Physical):

Today's Epiphany:

I Trust God With:

I Have Released:

I Am Starting To: ____.

My Miracle Notes

Miracle Positioning

Morning Positioning

Date:

My Intention:

Today's Affirmation:

Today I Am Asking God For:

I Am Grateful For:

Today I Will:

I See Myself (Write What You Envision Yourself Doing Today):

Nightly Positioning

I Am Feeling:

Time:

Today's Miracle (Describe It And How You Felt Receiving It):

Today's Work (Mental, Spiritual And/ Or Physical):

I Trust God With:

Today I Felt Led To:

Today's Epiphany:

I Have Released:

I Am Starting To: ____.

His Timing is A Miracle.

Miracle Positioning

Morning Positioning

Date:

My Intention:

Today's Affirmation:

Today I Am Asking God For:

I Am Grateful For:

Today I Will:

I See Myself (Write What You Envision Yourself Doing Today):

Nightly Positioning

I Am Feeling:

Time:

Today's Miracle (Describe It And How You Felt Receiving It):

Today's Work (Mental, Spiritual And/ Or Physical):

I Trust God With:

Today I Felt Led To:

Today's Epiphany:

I Have Released:

I Am Starting To: ____.

Miracle Positioning

Morning Positioning

Date:

My Intention:

Today's Affirmation:

Today I Will:

Today I Am Asking God For:

I See Myself (Write What You Envision Yourself Doing Today):

I Am Grateful For:

Nightly Positioning

I Am Feeling:

Time:

Today's Miracle (Describe It And How You Felt Receiving It):

Today I Felt Led To:

Today's Work (Mental, Spiritual And/ Or Physical):

Today's Epiphany:

I Trust God With:

I Have Released:

I Am Starting To: ____.

Miracle Positioning

Morning Positioning

Date:

My Intention:

Today's Affirmation:

Today I Am Asking God For:

I Am Grateful For:

Today I Will:

I See Myself (Write What You Envision Yourself Doing Today):

Nightly Positioning

I Am Feeling:

Time:

Today's Miracle (Describe It And How You Felt Receiving It):

Today's Work (Mental, Spiritual And/ Or Physical):

I Trust God With:

Today I Felt Led To:

Today's Epiphany:

I Have Released:

I Am Starting To: ____.

Miracle Positioning

Morning Positioning

Date:

My Intention:

Today's Affirmation:

Today I Am Asking God For:

I Am Grateful For:

Today I Will:

I See Myself (Write What You Envision Yourself Doing Today):

Nightly Positioning

I Am Feeling:

Time:

Today's Miracle (Describe It And How You Felt Receiving It):

Today's Work (Mental, Spiritual And/ Or Physical):

I Trust God With:

Today I Felt Led To:

Today's Epiphany:

I Have Released:

I Am Starting To: ____.

5 fears That Are Blocking My Best from Showing Up....

1:

2:

3:

4:

5:

i Am Getting What i Am Ready for.

Miracle Positioning

Morning Positioning

Date:

My Intention:

Today's Affirmation:

Today I Am Asking God For:

I Am Grateful For:

Today I Will:

I See Myself (Write What You Envision Yourself Doing Today):

Nightly Positioning

I Am Feeling:

Time:

Today's Miracle (Describe It And How You Felt Receiving It):

Today's Work (Mental, Spiritual And/ Or Physical):

I Trust God With:

Today I Felt Led To:

Today's Epiphany:

I Have Released:

I Am Starting To: ____.

Miracle Positioning

Morning Positioning

Date:

My Intention:

Today's Affirmation:

Today I Am Asking God For:

I Am Grateful For:

Today I Will:

I See Myself (Write What You Envision Yourself Doing Today):

Nightly Positioning

I Am Feeling:

Time:

Today's Miracle (Describe It And How You Felt Receiving It):

Today's Work (Mental, Spiritual And/ Or Physical):

I Trust God With:

Today I Felt Led To:

Today's Epiphany:

I Have Released:

I Am Starting To: ____.

Miracle Positioning

Morning Positioning

Date:

My Intention:

Today's Affirmation:

Today I Am Asking God For:

I Am Grateful For:

Today I Will:

I See Myself (Write What You Envision Yourself Doing Today):

Nightly Positioning

I Am Feeling:

Time:

Today's Miracle (Describe It And How You Felt Receiving It):

Today's Work (Mental, Spiritual And/ Or Physical):

I Trust God With:

Today I Felt Led To:

Today's Epiphany:

I Have Released:

I Am Starting To: ____.

My Miracle Notes

Miracle Positioning

Morning Positioning

Date:

My Intention:

Today's Affirmation:

Today I Will:

Today I Am Asking God For:

I See Myself (Write What You Envision Yourself Doing Today):

I Am Grateful For:

Nightly Positioning

I Am Feeling:

Time:

Today's Miracle (Describe It And How You Felt Receiving It):

Today I Felt Led To:

Today's Work (Mental, Spiritual And/ Or Physical):

Today's Epiphany:

I Trust God With:

I Have Released:

I Am Starting To: ______________________________.

it's Okay

To Be

Optimistic.

i Am Grateful.

Miracle Positioning

Morning Positioning

Date:

My Intention:

Today's Affirmation:

Today I Am Asking God For:

I Am Grateful For:

Today I Will:

I See Myself (Write What You Envision Yourself Doing Today):

Nightly Positioning

I Am Feeling:

Time:

Today's Miracle (Describe It And How You Felt Receiving It):

Today's Work (Mental, Spiritual And/ Or Physical):

I Trust God With:

Today I Felt Led To:

Today's Epiphany:

I Have Released:

I Am Starting To: ____.

Miracle Positioning

Morning Positioning

Date:

My Intention:

Today's Affirmation:

Today I Will:

Today I Am Asking God For:

I See Myself (Write What You Envision Yourself Doing Today):

I Am Grateful For:

Nightly Positioning

I Am Feeling:

Time:

Today's Miracle (Describe It And How You Felt Receiving It):

Today I Felt Led To:

Today's Work (Mental, Spiritual And/ Or Physical):

Today's Epiphany:

I Trust God With:

I Have Released:

I Am Starting To: ____.

Miracle Positioning

Morning Positioning

Date:

My Intention:

Today's Affirmation:

Today I Am Asking God For:

I Am Grateful For:

Today I Will:

I See Myself (Write What You Envision Yourself Doing Today):

Nightly Positioning

I Am Feeling:

Time:

Today's Miracle (Describe It And How You Felt Receiving It):

Today's Work (Mental, Spiritual And/ Or Physical):

I Trust God With:

Today I Felt Led To:

Today's Epiphany:

I Have Released:

I Am Starting To: ____.

7 Things That i Know Are Not True....

1:

2:

3:

4:

5:

6:

7:

My Dreams Will Come True.

Miracle Positioning

Morning Positioning

Date:

My Intention:

Today's Affirmation:

Today I Am Asking God For:

I Am Grateful For:

Today I Will:

I See Myself (Write What You Envision Yourself Doing Today):

Nightly Positioning

I Am Feeling:

Time:

Today's Miracle (Describe It And How You Felt Receiving It):

Today's Work (Mental, Spiritual And/ Or Physical):

I Trust God With:

Today I Felt Led To:

Today's Epiphany:

I Have Released:

I Am Starting To: ____.

i Operate in faith By....

Miracle Positioning

Morning Positioning

Date:

My Intention:

Today's Affirmation:

Today I Am Asking God For:

I Am Grateful For:

Today I Will:

I See Myself (Write What You Envision Yourself Doing Today):

Nightly Positioning

I Am Feeling:

Time:

Today's Miracle (Describe It And How You Felt Receiving It):

Today's Work (Mental, Spiritual And/ Or Physical):

I Trust God With:

Today I Felt Led To:

Today's Epiphany:

I Have Released:

I Am Starting To: ____.

Miracle Positioning

Morning Positioning

Date:

My Intention:

Today's Affirmation:

Today I Will:

Today I Am Asking God For:

I See Myself (Write What You Envision Yourself Doing Today):

I Am Grateful For:

Nightly Positioning

I Am Feeling:

Time:

Today's Miracle (Describe It And How You Felt Receiving It):

Today I Felt Led To:

Today's Work (Mental, Spiritual And/ Or Physical):

Today's Epiphany:

I Trust God With:

I Have Released:

I Am Starting To: ____.

Miracle Positioning

Morning Positioning

Date:

My Intention:

Today's Affirmation:

Today I Am Asking God For:

I Am Grateful For:

Today I Will:

I See Myself (Write What You Envision Yourself Doing Today):

Nightly Positioning

I Am Feeling:

Time:

Today's Miracle (Describe It And How You Felt Receiving It):

Today's Work (Mental, Spiritual And/ Or Physical):

I Trust God With:

Today I Felt Led To:

Today's Epiphany:

I Have Released:

I Am Starting To: ____.

My Miracle Notes

Miracle Positioning

Morning Positioning

Date:

My Intention:

Today's Affirmation:

Today I Am Asking God For:

I Am Grateful For:

Today I Will:

I See Myself (Write What You Envision Yourself Doing Today):

Nightly Positioning

I Am Feeling:

Time:

Today's Miracle (Describe It And How You Felt Receiving It):

Today's Work (Mental, Spiritual And/ Or Physical):

I Trust God With:

Today I Felt Led To:

Today's Epiphany:

I Have Released:

I Am Starting To: ____.

Miracle Positioning

Morning Positioning

Date:

My Intention:

Today's Affirmation:

Today I Will:

Today I Am Asking God For:

I See Myself (Write What You Envision Yourself Doing Today):

I Am Grateful For:

Nightly Positioning

I Am Feeling:

Time:

Today's Miracle (Describe It And How You Felt Receiving It):

Today I Felt Led To:

Today's Work (Mental, Spiritual And/ Or Physical):

Today's Epiphany:

I Trust God With:

I Have Released:

I Am Starting To: ____.

Miracle Positioning

Morning Positioning

Date:

My Intention:

Today's Affirmation:

Today I Am Asking God For:

I Am Grateful For:

Today I Will:

I See Myself (Write What You Envision Yourself Doing Today):

Nightly Positioning

I Am Feeling:

Time:

Today's Miracle (Describe It And How You Felt Receiving It):

Today's Work (Mental, Spiritual And/ Or Physical):

I Trust God With:

Today I Felt Led To:

Today's Epiphany:

I Have Released:

I Am Starting To: ____.

My Miracles Will Keep Coming Until i Stop Believing In Them.

Miracle Positioning

Morning Positioning

Date:

My Intention:

Today's Affirmation:

Today I Am Asking God For:

I Am Grateful For:

Today I Will:

I See Myself (Write What You Envision Yourself Doing Today):

Nightly Positioning

I Am Feeling:

Time:

Today's Miracle (Describe It And How You Felt Receiving It):

Today's Work (Mental, Spiritual And/ Or Physical):

I Trust God With:

Today I Felt Led To:

Today's Epiphany:

I Have Released:

I Am Starting To: ____.

Miracle Positioning

Morning Positioning

Date:

My Intention:

Today's Affirmation:

Today I Am Asking God For:

I Am Grateful For:

Today I Will:

I See Myself (Write What You Envision Yourself Doing Today):

Nightly Positioning

I Am Feeling:

Time:

Today's Miracle (Describe It And How You Felt Receiving It):

Today's Work (Mental, Spiritual And/ Or Physical):

I Trust God With:

Today I Felt Led To:

Today's Epiphany:

I Have Released:

I Am Starting To: ____.

His Miracles Doesn't Have A Limit.

When i Quiet My Mind, i....

Miracle Positioning

Morning Positioning

Date:

My Intention:

Today's Affirmation:

Today I Will:

Today I Am Asking God For:

I See Myself (Write What You Envision Yourself Doing Today):

I Am Grateful For:

Nightly Positioning

I Am Feeling:

Time:

Today's Miracle (Describe It And How You Felt Receiving It):

Today I Felt Led To:

Today's Work (Mental, Spiritual And/ Or Physical):

Today's Epiphany:

I Trust God With:

I Have Released:

I Am Starting To: ____.

Miracle Positioning

Morning Positioning

Date:

My Intention:

Today's Affirmation:

Today I Am Asking God For:

I Am Grateful For:

Today I Will:

I See Myself (Write What You Envision Yourself Doing Today):

Nightly Positioning

I Am Feeling:

Time:

Today's Miracle (Describe It And How You Felt Receiving It):

Today's Work (Mental, Spiritual And/ Or Physical):

I Trust God With:

Today I Felt Led To:

Today's Epiphany:

I Have Released:

I Am Starting To: ____.

My Blessings Didn't Come By Luck.

Miracle Positioning

Morning Positioning

Date:

My Intention:

Today's Affirmation:

Today I Am Asking God For:

I Am Grateful For:

Today I Will:

I See Myself (Write What You Envision Yourself Doing Today):

Nightly Positioning

I Am Feeling:

Time:

Today's Miracle (Describe It And How You Felt Receiving It):

Today's Work (Mental, Spiritual And/ Or Physical):

I Trust God With:

Today I Felt Led To:

Today's Epiphany:

I Have Released:

I Am Starting To: ____.

Miracle Positioning

Morning Positioning

Date:

My Intention:

Today's Affirmation:

Today I Am Asking God For:

I Am Grateful For:

Today I Will:

I See Myself (Write What You Envision Yourself Doing Today):

Nightly Positioning

I Am Feeling:

Time:

Today's Miracle (Describe It And How You Felt Receiving It):

Today's Work (Mental, Spiritual And/ Or Physical):

I Trust God With:

Today I Felt Led To:

Today's Epiphany:

I Have Released:

I Am Starting To: ____.

My Miracle Notes

Miracle Positioning

Morning Positioning

Date:

My Intention:

Today's Affirmation:

Today I Will:

Today I Am Asking God For:

I See Myself (Write What You Envision Yourself Doing Today):

I Am Grateful For:

Nightly Positioning

I Am Feeling:

Time:

Today's Miracle (Describe It And How You Felt Receiving It):

Today I Felt Led To:

Today's Work (Mental, Spiritual And/ Or Physical):

Today's Epiphany:

I Trust God With:

I Have Released:

I Am Starting To: ____.

Miracle Positioning

Morning Positioning

Date:

My Intention:

Today's Affirmation:

Today I Am Asking God For:

I Am Grateful For:

Today I Will:

I See Myself (Write What You Envision Yourself Doing Today):

Nightly Positioning

I Am Feeling:

Time:

Today's Miracle (Describe It And How You Felt Receiving It):

Today's Work (Mental, Spiritual And/ Or Physical):

I Trust God With:

Today I Felt Led To:

Today's Epiphany:

I Have Released:

I Am Starting To: ____.

Today i Will Walk With My Miracles in My Heart.

The Only Thing i'm Attached To.....

Miracle Positioning

Morning Positioning

Date:

My Intention:

Today's Affirmation:

Today I Am Asking God For:

I Am Grateful For:

Today I Will:

I See Myself (Write What You Envision Yourself Doing Today):

Nightly Positioning

I Am Feeling:

Time:

Today's Miracle (Describe It And How You Felt Receiving It):

Today's Work (Mental, Spiritual And/ Or Physical):

I Trust God With:

Today I Felt Led To:

Today's Epiphany:

I Have Released:

I Am Starting To: ____.

Miracle Positioning

Morning Positioning

Date:

My Intention:

Today's Affirmation:

Today I Am Asking God For:

I Am Grateful For:

Today I Will:

I See Myself (Write What You Envision Yourself Doing Today):

Nightly Positioning

I Am Feeling:

Time:

Today's Miracle (Describe It And How You Felt Receiving It):

Today's Work (Mental, Spiritual And/ Or Physical):

I Trust God With:

Today I Felt Led To:

Today's Epiphany:

I Have Released:

I Am Starting To: ____.

Miracle Positioning

Morning Positioning

Date:

My Intention:

Today's Affirmation:

Today I Am Asking God For:

I Am Grateful For:

Today I Will:

I See Myself (Write What You Envision Yourself Doing Today):

Nightly Positioning

I Am Feeling:

Time:

Today's Miracle (Describe It And How You Felt Receiving It):

Today's Work (Mental, Spiritual And/ Or Physical):

I Trust God With:

Today I Felt Led To:

Today's Epiphany:

I Have Released:

I Am Starting To: ____.

i Am A Creator.

I Remember When He Stepped In With A Miracle.

Miracle Positioning

Morning Positioning

Date:

My Intention:

Today's Affirmation:

Today I Am Asking God For:

I Am Grateful For:

Today I Will:

I See Myself (Write What You Envision Yourself Doing Today):

Nightly Positioning

I Am Feeling:

Time:

Today's Miracle (Describe It And How You Felt Receiving It):

Today's Work (Mental, Spiritual And/ Or Physical):

I Trust God With:

Today I Felt Led To:

Today's Epiphany:

I Have Released:

I Am Starting To: ____.

Miracle Positioning

Morning Positioning

Date:

My Intention:

Today's Affirmation:

Today I Am Asking God For:

I Am Grateful For:

Today I Will:

I See Myself (Write What You Envision Yourself Doing Today):

Nightly Positioning

I Am Feeling:

Time:

Today's Miracle (Describe It And How You Felt Receiving It):

Today's Work (Mental, Spiritual And/ Or Physical):

I Trust God With:

Today I Felt Led To:

Today's Epiphany:

I Have Released:

I Am Starting To: ____.

Miracle Positioning

Morning Positioning

Date:

My Intention:

Today's Affirmation:

Today I Am Asking God For:

I Am Grateful For:

Today I Will:

I See Myself (Write What You Envision Yourself Doing Today):

Nightly Positioning

I Am Feeling:

Time:

Today's Miracle (Describe It And How You Felt Receiving It):

Today's Work (Mental, Spiritual And/ Or Physical):

I Trust God With:

Today I Felt Led To:

Today's Epiphany:

I Have Released:

I Am Starting To: ______________________________.

The ideal Scenario To Something i Want....

My Miracle Notes

Miracle Positioning

Morning Positioning

Date:

My Intention:

Today's Affirmation:

Today I Am Asking God For:

I Am Grateful For:

Today I Will:

I See Myself (Write What You Envision Yourself Doing Today):

Nightly Positioning

I Am Feeling:

Time:

Today's Miracle (Describe It And How You Felt Receiving It):

Today's Work (Mental, Spiritual And/ Or Physical):

I Trust God With:

Today I Felt Led To:

Today's Epiphany:

I Have Released:

I Am Starting To: ______________________________.

Miracle Positioning

Morning Positioning

Date:

My Intention:

Today's Affirmation:

Today I Am Asking God For:

I Am Grateful For:

Today I Will:

I See Myself (Write What You Envision Yourself Doing Today):

Nightly Positioning

I Am Feeling:

Time:

Today's Miracle (Describe It And How You Felt Receiving It):

Today's Work (Mental, Spiritual And/ Or Physical):

I Trust God With:

Today I Felt Led To:

Today's Epiphany:

I Have Released:

I Am Starting To: ____.

Miracle Positioning

Morning Positioning

Date:

My Intention:

Today's Affirmation:

Today I Am Asking God For:

I Am Grateful For:

Today I Will:

I See Myself (Write What You Envision Yourself Doing Today):

Nightly Positioning

I Am Feeling:

Time:

Today's Miracle (Describe It And How You Felt Receiving It):

Today's Work (Mental, Spiritual And/ Or Physical):

I Trust God With:

Today I Felt Led To:

Today's Epiphany:

I Have Released:

I Am Starting To: ______________________________.

Miracle Positioning

Morning Positioning

Date:

My Intention:

Today's Affirmation:

Today I Am Asking God For:

I Am Grateful For:

Today I Will:

I See Myself (Write What You Envision Yourself Doing Today):

Nightly Positioning

I Am Feeling:

Time:

Today's Miracle (Describe It And How You Felt Receiving It):

Today's Work (Mental, Spiritual And/ Or Physical):

I Trust God With:

Today I Felt Led To:

Today's Epiphany:

I Have Released:

I Am Starting To: ____.

I'm More
Than Happy
To Let Life
Surprise
Me.

I Am in Harmony With....

Miracle Positioning

Morning Positioning

Date:

My Intention:

Today's Affirmation:

Today I Am Asking God For:

I Am Grateful For:

Today I Will:

I See Myself (Write What You Envision Yourself Doing Today):

Nightly Positioning

I Am Feeling:

Time:

Today's Miracle (Describe It And How You Felt Receiving It):

Today's Work (Mental, Spiritual And/ Or Physical):

I Trust God With:

Today I Felt Led To:

Today's Epiphany:

I Have Released:

I Am Starting To: ______________________________.

Miracle Positioning

Morning Positioning

Date:

My Intention:

Today's Affirmation:

Today I Am Asking God For:

I Am Grateful For:

Today I Will:

I See Myself (Write What You Envision Yourself Doing Today):

Nightly Positioning

I Am Feeling:

Time:

Today's Miracle (Describe It And How You Felt Receiving It):

Today's Work (Mental, Spiritual And/ Or Physical):

I Trust God With:

Today I Felt Led To:

Today's Epiphany:

I Have Released:

I Am Starting To: ______________________________.

My faith is Getting Stronger And Stronger.

i Love How My Miracles Love Me for Who i Am And Always Show Up.

Miracle Positioning

Morning Positioning

Date:

My Intention:

Today's Affirmation:

Today I Am Asking God For:

I Am Grateful For:

Today I Will:

I See Myself (Write What You Envision Yourself Doing Today):

Nightly Positioning

I Am Feeling:

Time:

Today's Miracle (Describe It And How You Felt Receiving It):

Today's Work (Mental, Spiritual And/Or Physical):

I Trust God With:

Today I Felt Led To:

Today's Epiphany:

I Have Released:

I Am Starting To: ____.

Miracle Positioning

Morning Positioning

Date:

My Intention:

Today's Affirmation:

Today I Am Asking God For:

I Am Grateful For:

Today I Will:

I See Myself (Write What You Envision Yourself Doing Today):

Nightly Positioning

I Am Feeling:

Time:

Today's Miracle (Describe It And How You Felt Receiving It):

Today's Work (Mental, Spiritual And/Or Physical):

I Trust God With:

Today I Felt Led To:

Today's Epiphany:

I Have Released:

I Am Starting To: ____.

Miracle Positioning

Morning Positioning

Date:

My Intention:

Today's Affirmation:

Today I Will:

Today I Am Asking God For:

I See Myself (Write What You Envision Yourself Doing Today):

I Am Grateful For:

Nightly Positioning

I Am Feeling:

Time:

Today's Miracle (Describe It And How You Felt Receiving It):

Today I Felt Led To:

Today's Work (Mental, Spiritual And/ Or Physical):

Today's Epiphany:

I Trust God With:

I Have Released:

I Am Starting To: ____.

i Am Choosing To Live....

Learning to Believe, Not to Doubt.

Miracle Positioning

Morning Positioning

Date:

My Intention:

Today's Affirmation:

Today I Am Asking God For:

I Am Grateful For:

Today I Will:

I See Myself (Write What You Envision Yourself Doing Today):

Nightly Positioning

I Am Feeling:

Time:

Today's Miracle (Describe It And How You Felt Receiving It):

Today's Work (Mental, Spiritual And/ Or Physical):

I Trust God With:

Today I Felt Led To:

Today's Epiphany:

I Have Released:

I Am Starting To: ____.

Miracle Positioning

Morning Positioning

Date:

My Intention:

Today's Affirmation:

Today I Am Asking God For:

I Am Grateful For:

Today I Will:

I See Myself (Write What You Envision Yourself Doing Today):

Nightly Positioning

I Am Feeling:

Time:

Today's Miracle (Describe It And How You Felt Receiving It):

Today's Work (Mental, Spiritual And/ Or Physical):

I Trust God With:

Today I Felt Led To:

Today's Epiphany:

I Have Released:

I Am Starting To: ______________________________.

Miracle Positioning

Morning Positioning

Date:

My Intention:

Today's Affirmation:

Today I Am Asking God For:

I Am Grateful For:

Today I Will:

I See Myself (Write What You Envision Yourself Doing Today):

Nightly Positioning

I Am Feeling:

Time:

Today's Miracle (Describe It And How You Felt Receiving It):

Today's Work (Mental, Spiritual And/ Or Physical):

I Trust God With:

Today I Felt Led To:

Today's Epiphany:

I Have Released:

I Am Starting To: ____.

I'm In Love With What i Am Manifesting.

Miracle Positioning

Morning Positioning

Date:

My Intention:

Today's Affirmation:

Today I Am Asking God For:

I Am Grateful For:

Today I Will:

I See Myself (Write What You Envision Yourself Doing Today):

Nightly Positioning

I Am Feeling:

Time:

Today's Miracle (Describe It And How You Felt Receiving It):

Today's Work (Mental, Spiritual And/ Or Physical):

I Trust God With:

Today I Felt Led To:

Today's Epiphany:

I Have Released:

I Am Starting To: ______________________________.

Miracle Positioning

Morning Positioning

Date:

My Intention:

Today's Affirmation:

Today I Will:

Today I Am Asking God For:

I See Myself (Write What You Envision Yourself Doing Today):

I Am Grateful For:

Nightly Positioning

I Am Feeling:

Time:

Today's Miracle (Describe It And How You Felt Receiving It):

Today I Felt Led To:

Today's Work (Mental, Spiritual And/ Or Physical):

Today's Epiphany:

I Trust God With:

I Have Released:

I Am Starting To: ______________________________.

Miracle Positioning

Morning Positioning

Date:

My Intention:

Today's Affirmation:

Today I Am Asking God For:

I Am Grateful For:

Today I Will:

I See Myself (Write What You Envision Yourself Doing Today):

Nightly Positioning

I Am Feeling:

Time:

Today's Miracle (Describe It And How You Felt Receiving It):

Today's Work (Mental, Spiritual And/ Or Physical):

I Trust God With:

Today I Felt Led To:

Today's Epiphany:

I Have Released:

I Am Starting To: ____.

i Will Not Be Distracted from My Miracles.

My Miracle Notes

Miracle Positioning

Morning Positioning

Date:

My Intention:

Today's Affirmation:

Today I Am Asking God For:

I Am Grateful For:

Today I Will:

I See Myself (Write What You Envision Yourself Doing Today):

Nightly Positioning

I Am Feeling:

Time:

Today's Miracle (Describe It And How You Felt Receiving It):

Today's Work (Mental, Spiritual And/ Or Physical):

I Trust God With:

Today I Felt Led To:

Today's Epiphany:

I Have Released:

I Am Starting To: ____.

Miracle Positioning

Morning Positioning

Date:

My Intention:

Today's Affirmation:

Today I Am Asking God For:

I Am Grateful For:

Today I Will:

I See Myself (Write What You Envision Yourself Doing Today):

Nightly Positioning

I Am Feeling:

Time:

Today's Miracle (Describe It And How You Felt Receiving It):

Today's Work (Mental, Spiritual And/ Or Physical):

I Trust God With:

Today I Felt Led To:

Today's Epiphany:

I Have Released:

I Am Starting To: ______________________________.

Miracle Positioning

Morning Positioning

Date:

My Intention:

Today's Affirmation:

Today I Will:

Today I Am Asking God For:

I See Myself (Write What You Envision Yourself Doing Today):

I Am Grateful For:

Nightly Positioning

I Am Feeling:

Time:

Today's Miracle (Describe It And How You Felt Receiving It):

Today I Felt Led To:

Today's Work (Mental, Spiritual And/ Or Physical):

Today's Epiphany:

I Trust God With:

I Have Released:

I Am Starting To: ____.

Miracle Positioning

Morning Positioning

Date:

My Intention:

Today's Affirmation:

Today I Am Asking God For:

I Am Grateful For:

Today I Will:

I See Myself (Write What You Envision Yourself Doing Today):

Nightly Positioning

I Am Feeling:

Time:

Today's Miracle (Describe It And How You Felt Receiving It):

Today's Work (Mental, Spiritual And/ Or Physical):

I Trust God With:

Today I Felt Led To:

Today's Epiphany:

I Have Released:

I Am Starting To: ______________________________.

I feel
The Love.
I feel His
Love.

Made in the USA
Columbia, SC
21 August 2021